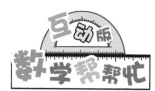

倒霉蛋布拉德

[美]盖尔·赫尔曼◎著

[美]斯黛芬妮·罗斯◎绘

范晓星◎译

天津出版传媒集团

新蕾出版社

图书在版编目 (CIP) 数据

倒霉蛋布拉德/(美)盖尔·赫尔曼(Gail Herman)
著;(美)斯黛芬妮·罗斯(Stephanie Roth)绘;范
晓星译.-- 天津:新蕾出版社,2016.9(2024.12 重印)
(数学帮帮忙·互动版)
书名原文:Bad Luck Brad
ISBN 978-7-5307-6471-8

Ⅰ.①倒… Ⅱ.①盖… ②斯… ③范… Ⅲ.①数学-
儿童读物 Ⅳ.①O1-49

中国版本图书馆 CIP 数据核字(2016)第 201536 号

Bad Luck Brad by Gail Herman;
Illustrated by Stephanie Roth.
Copyright ⓒ 2002 by Kane Press, Inc.
All rights reserved, including the right of reproduction in whole or in part in any
form. This edition published by arrangement with Kane Press, Inc. New York, NY,
represented by Lerner Publishing Group through The ChoiceMaker Korea Co.
agency.
Simplified Chinese translation copyright ⓒ 2016 by New Buds Publishing House
(Tianjin) Limited Company
ALL RIGHTS RESERVED
本书中文简体版专有出版权经由中华版权代理中心授予新蕾出版社(天津)有
限公司。未经许可,不得以任何方式复制或抄袭本书的任何部分。
津图登字:02-2012-218

出版发行:天津出版传媒集团
　　　　　新蕾出版社
http://www.newbuds.com.cn
地　　址:天津市和平区西康路 35 号(300051)
出 版 人:马玉秀
电　　话:总编办(022)23332422
　　　　　发行部(022)23332679　23332351
传　　真:(022)23332422
经　　销:全国新华书店
印　　刷:天津新华印务有限公司
开　　本:787mm×1092mm　1/16
印　　张:3
版　　次:2016 年 9 月第 1 版　2024 年 12 月第 20 次印刷
定　　价:12.00 元

无处不在的数学

资深编辑　卢　江

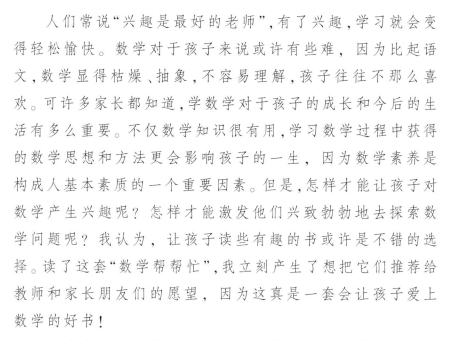

　　人们常说"兴趣是最好的老师",有了兴趣,学习就会变得轻松愉快。数学对于孩子来说或许有些难,因为比起语文,数学显得枯燥、抽象,不容易理解,孩子往往不那么喜欢。可许多家长都知道,学数学对于孩子的成长和今后的生活有多么重要。不仅数学知识很有用,学习数学过程中获得的数学思想和方法更会影响孩子的一生,因为数学素养是构成人基本素质的一个重要因素。但是,怎样才能让孩子对数学产生兴趣呢?怎样才能激发他们兴致勃勃地去探索数学问题呢?我认为,让孩子读些有趣的书或许是不错的选择。读了这套"数学帮帮忙",我立刻产生了想把它们推荐给教师和家长朋友们的愿望,因为这真是一套会让孩子爱上数学的好书!

　　这套有趣的图书从美国引进,原出版者是美国资深教育专家。每本书讲述一个孩子们生活中的故事,由故事中出现的问题自然地引入一个数学知识,然后通过运用数学知识解决问题。比如,从帮助外婆整理散落的纽扣引出分类,从为小狗记录藏骨头的地点引出空间方位等等。故事素材全部来源于孩子们的真实生活，不是童话，不是幻想，而是鲜活的生活实例。正是这些发生在孩子身边的故事，让孩子们懂得，数学无处不在并且非常有用；这些鲜活的实例也使得抽象的概念更易于理解，更容易激发孩子学习数学的兴趣，让他们逐渐爱上数学。这样的教育思想和方法与我国近年来提倡的数学教育理念是十分吻合的！

　　这是一套适合5~8岁孩子阅读的书，书中的有趣情节和生动的插画可以将抽象的数学问题直观化、形象化，为孩子的思维活动提供具体形象的支持。如果亲子共读的话，家长可以带领孩子推测情节的发展，探讨解决难题的办法，让孩子在愉悦的氛围中学到知识和方法。

　　值得教师和家长朋友们注意的是，在每本书的后面，出版者还加入了"互动课堂"及"互动练习"，一方面通过一些精心设计的活动让孩子巩固新学到的数学知识，进一步体会知识的含义和实际应用；另一方面帮助家长指导孩子阅读，体会故事中数学之外的道理，逐步提升孩子的阅读理解能力。

　　我相信孩子读过这套书后一定会明白，原来，数学不是烦恼，不是包袱，数学真能帮大忙！

布拉德揉揉眼睛从床上坐了起来,一看表,7:45 了!

"哎呀!糟糕!"他大喊一声。睡过头了!今天是这学期最后一天,学校里还有联欢会什么的呢!

3

布拉德赶忙跑下楼。

他在楼梯上撞到了
妹妹劳伦和弟弟亚当。

然后，他又一脚踩上了玩具汽车。
"天哪，真倒霉！"他自言自语地说。

布拉德最后一个走进厨房。

爸爸说:"看起来大家都睡过头了,吃不上鸡蛋和煎饼了。"

妈妈拿出一袋早餐饼干说:"来,每人拿一块吧。"

饼干的包装袋上写着"清香柠檬、味浓巧克力"两种口味。不过布拉德知道,袋子里面巧克力口味的一定不多了,因为大部分已经被他吃掉了。

　　"我要味浓巧克力的!"亚当嚷道。

　　"我也要!"劳伦嚷道。

　　"我也是!"布拉德也嚷道。

　　大家都伸手去抓。

　　"别抢!"妈妈说着摇晃了一下饼干袋。所有的饼干都被倒了出来:有很多柠檬口味的,但只有两块巧克力口味的。

　　"哎呀!"布拉德说,"两块巧克力口味的,可我们三个都想要啊!"他祈祷自己好运。

　　"还是公平一些吧。"妈妈说完,把饼干放回包装袋里,"你们每人只许拿一块,劳伦先走进厨房的,你先拿,然后是亚当,最后是布拉德。谁都不许偷看哟!"

劳伦把手伸进去,掏出一看说:"唉!是柠檬口味的!"

"该我了!"亚当说着也摸出一块。"好幸运啊!"他欢呼起来,"巧克力口味的!"

布拉德想，袋子里只剩一块巧克力的了。他把手伸进口袋。"倒霉。"他说，"柠檬口味的。"

布拉德叹了口气。他原本以为这学期最后一天一定会开开心心呢！可怎么什么都不对劲！

妈妈把布拉德和他的朋友皮特一起送到
学校。"放学以后我到糖果机游戏店接你们。"
她说,"然后我带你们去做些特别的事!"
　　"去看电影怎么样?"布拉德问。
　　"可以啊!"妈妈回答。

"我们去看《遨游太空》第五部吧。"布拉
德说,"前面四部我都喜欢!"

"不好!"皮特说,"我想看《恐龙时代》!"

"《遨游太空》！"他们整理课本的时候，
布拉德这样说。

"《恐龙时代》！"他们清理课桌的时候，
皮特这样说。

"联欢会就要开始了！"科斯塔太太宣布，"大家把各自准备的神秘礼物放在桌子上吧。"

　　"好！"布拉德兴奋地喊道。

布拉德准备的礼物是一个星球战士的玩具,那是电影《遨游太空》里面的人物。他特别想抽到自己的礼物。

　　皮特小声告诉他:"我带的是霸王龙!"

　　"真棒!"布拉德说。

　　布拉德很好奇其他同学准备的是什么礼
物。保罗的礼物用恐龙花样的包装纸包着。
他听到扎克说："我的礼物是星球战士！"

　　"好东西还不少哟！"布拉德说，"也许我
的手气会很好！"

布拉德又听到丽萨小声对艾拉说："我带的是《小马巡游》里面的小小马。安妮、阿比和莎拉准备的也都是这个。"

"嗯。"布拉德说。他不想要一个傻傻的小小马。他不想要女孩子准备的礼物。

"抽取礼物的时间到了！"科斯塔太太宣布，"每个同学从这顶帽子里抽一张纸条，看看上面写着谁的名字，然后到桌子那边，拿那个同学准备的礼物！"

同学们都排队站好。

布拉德一个劲儿地盯着那些礼物。可是，他突然发现了一个问题：班里的女孩比男孩多！这就是说，他抽到女生名字的可能性比抽到男生名字的可能性大！"没准儿我会得到小小马。"他咕哝道，"而不是得到我真正想要的礼物。"

轮到布拉德了。他抽出了一张纸条，上面写着：阿比。"哦，不！"他说，"我得到的准是小小马。"但他还是拆开了礼物。

"你好幸运啊！"莎拉尖声大叫，"那是《小马巡游》里面最漂亮的小小马！"

幸运？布拉德可不这么想。他觉得自己是"倒霉蛋布拉德"。

艾拉拆开了她的礼物。"星球战士！"她说，"我做梦都想要一个呢！"

布拉德叹了口气。

"布拉德！"丽萨说，"我抽到你的名字啦！你带的是什么礼物啊？"

　　"星球战士！"布拉德回答。

　　丽萨做了个鬼脸。

　　"嘿！"布拉德提议，"你想交换吗？"

　　"当然好呀！"丽萨回答。

　　这时，下课铃响了。放假了！快乐的暑假开始了！

布拉德和皮特飞快地跑到糖果机游戏店。皮特说："我想吃酸桃味的霸王龙软糖！"

"我想要泡泡糖。"布拉德说，"红色的。"

布拉德看着糖果机里的泡泡糖。第一台糖果机里面白色的最多。第二台里面大多是黄色和紫色的。第三台糖果机里有白色、黄色、紫色、绿色、黑色和红色的！

皮特把最后一点儿霸王龙软糖咽下肚。"我还要买一块白色的泡泡糖。"他说着往第一个糖果机里投了一枚 25 美分的硬币，从糖果机里掉出来一块白色的泡泡糖。

　　布拉德往第三个糖果机里也投了一枚 25 美分的硬币。"红色！红色！"他喊。叮当！从里面掉出了一块白色的泡泡糖。

　　布拉德把泡泡糖送给了皮特，说："你真
走运！总是能得到想要的,都两次了！"

　　皮特狡黠地笑道："因为我先看好哪个糖
果机里面我喜欢的那种颜色多啊！"

　　"我也懂。"布拉德说,"可这三台糖果机,
哪个里面的红色泡泡糖也不是很多啊。所
以,我可能得不到红色的泡泡糖了。"

"你不是也喜欢紫色的吗？"皮特说，"这台糖果机里有不少紫色的！"

"那我试试！"布拉德说着，把自己最后一枚 25 美分的硬币投了进去。结果呢？一块黄色的泡泡糖！

皮特摇摇头说："这种事好像谁也说不准的！给，我还有一枚硬币。"

"那我再碰碰运气吧！"布拉德说。

嘟！嘟！布拉德的妈妈来接他们了。

　　"来不及了。"皮特说,"走,咱们去看《恐龙时代》去吧!"

　　"不!"布拉德喊,"是《遨游太空》!"

　　两个小家伙奔向汽车。

"咱们去看看正在上映什么电影。"妈妈说，"我们要看下午 4:00 的那场。"

　　她翻开报纸，《遨游太空》在五家电影院上映，《恐龙时代》只在一家上映。

　　布拉德狡黠地一笑。他想，还是看《遨游太空》的机会大呀！好几家电影院都在放！

　　"《恐龙时代》下午5:15开始。"妈妈说，
"《遨游太空》有下午3:30、4:00、4:30、5:00和
5:30的场次。"

　　"您刚才说有下午4:00的！"布拉德高
兴地喊道，"那我们去看《遨游太空》了！"

　　皮特叹了一口气。

"对不起啦！"布拉德对皮特说。他特别
理解皮特现在的心情,这时他想起了什么。

"咱们下回再看《恐龙时代》！"布拉德安慰道，"还有好多机会呢！我们有长长的暑假！"

31

概　率

与其碰运气，不如动脑筋！

这几位同学中有一位将赢得班级绘画比赛第一名。

下面几句话都是正确的，你能解释一下吗？

● 女生得奖的可能性更大。

● 棕色眼睛的同学得奖的可能性更大。

请你闭上眼睛，从下面两个箱子里各摸出一件玩具。

你认为是从红箱子里摸出恐龙的机会大，还是从绿箱子里摸出恐龙的机会大？为什么？

亲爱的家长朋友，请您和孩子一起完成下面这些内容，会有更大的收获哟！

提高阅读能力

● 阅读封面，包括书名、作者等内容。请孩子猜一猜布拉德遇到了什么倒霉事呢？

● 布拉德一天里遇到了哪些倒霉事？他又遇到了哪些幸运的事？故事里发生的好事，是因为幸运的原因吗？

● 在第 19 页，布拉德觉得自己"没准儿会得到小小马"，在第 25 页，他认为自己"可能得不到红色的泡泡糖了"。他猜对了吗？"可能"是什么意思？

● 皮特告诉布拉德一个方法："因为我先看好哪个糖果机里面我喜欢的那种颜色多啊。"为什么这个想法很好？他的这个方法在故事里成功了吗？

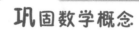

巩固数学概念

- 请利用第 32 页上的内容，讨论如下概念："概率""可能性很大""有可能"。一个女生赢得绘画比赛第一名的可能性是多大？是不是五个里面选出三个的可能性比五个里面选出两个的可能性大？

- 布拉德不想要"女孩子准备的礼物"，可为什么他抽到女生名字的可能性大呢？（提示：因为帽子里写着女孩名字的纸条比写着男孩名字的纸条多。）

- 请看第 7 页。图中画了几块巧克力口味的饼干？几块柠檬口味的？请孩子画三个饼干包装袋的图，在这些图里是可以看见袋子里面有什么饼干的。这三幅图要展现劳伦、亚当和布拉德拿饼干之前袋子里的情况。每个孩子伸手去拿的时候，包装袋里分别有几块巧克力口味的饼干？几块柠檬口味的饼干？谁拿到巧克力口味饼干的机会大？为什么？

生活中的数学

- 如果孩子想用糖果机买糖果的话，请他想想皮特的小窍门。也许你的孩子已经知道这个方法了！鼓励孩子用语言把这个方法描述一遍。

- 试试这个：用一个纸袋，装一些棋子或糖果，分别是两种颜色各一半。在孩子每次拿出一个棋子或糖果前，让他预测一下自己会拿到什么。如果他的预测准确，就请他保留这个棋子或糖果。可以允许他数一数口袋里还剩多少个棋子或糖果。正如布拉德在第 32 页所说："与其碰运气，不如动脑筋！"

小伙伴,下面的选择题你会做吗?

①有一个盒子,里面装着 4 个白色球和 5 个黄色球,从盒子中任意取出一个球,是( )的可能性较大。

　A. 白色球　　B. 蓝色球　　C. 黄色球

②有一盒白色棋子,从中任意摸出一个,( )是白色棋子。

　A. 可能　　　B. 一定　　　C. 不可能

③从 1 个蓝色玻璃球和 10 个白色玻璃球中任意摸出一个,摸到( )玻璃球的可能性更小一些。

　A. 白色　　　B. 蓝色　　　C. 红色

关于概率的知识,生活中如果不涉及具体的数值,也可以用"可能性"来描述,比如可能、一定、不可能……

天气情况记录

1	2	3	4	5	6	7
☀	☀	⛅	☀	☀	⛅	⛅
8	9	10	11	12	13	14
⛅	☀	☀	☀	☀	⛅	⛅
15	16	17	18	19	20	21
⛅	⛅	☀	☀	⛅	☀	☀
22	23	24	25	26	27	28
⛅	☀	☀	⛅	⛅	☁	☁
29	30	31				
🌧	🌧	🌧				

上面是我做的天气情况记录。你觉得，我漂亮的雨伞派上用场的机会多吗？你能用一个分数表示雨天的概率吗？

妈妈,我想吃根棒棒糖,可以吗?

可以呀,不过你只能从糖果盒里
摸一次,看你够不够幸运啦!

你知道布拉德的妈妈为什么说"看你
够不够幸运"吗?

你觉得布拉德最有可能摸到什么糖?

你有窍门帮他一次就摸出棒棒糖吗?

亲爱的小伙伴，概率可不只是碰运气哟，试着动脑筋来推理吧！

①在（　）色箱子里摸出铅笔的概率最大。

②在（　）色箱子里摸出橡皮的概率最大。

③在（　）色箱子里不可能摸出订书机。

④在（　）色箱子里能摸出刻刀。

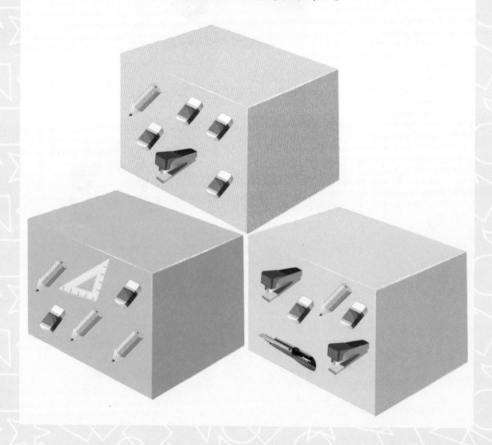

扑克游戏试试看

从一副扑克牌中取出的两组牌，分别是梅花A、梅花2、梅花3、梅花4和方块A、方块2、方块3、方块4,将它们背面朝上分别重新洗牌后，从两组牌中各摸出一张，那么摸出的两张牌的牌面数字之和等于5的概率是多少？

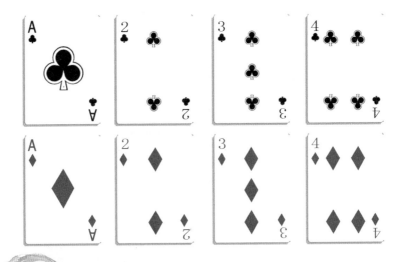

让我想一想，1+4、2+3……

不如试试原来学过的列表法吧，应该是个不错的选择！

学校要举行乒乓球比赛，每个班必须选派出一对男女混合双打选手参赛。从布拉德、皮特、丽萨、艾拉中选男、女生各一名组成一对选手参赛，有几种组合方式呢？如果布拉德和丽萨的组合是最强组合，那么采用随机抽签的办法，恰好选出布拉德和丽萨参赛的概率是多少？

最强组合

布拉德和皮特玩抛硬币的游戏，他们将两枚一元硬币抛向空中，落下后，如果硬币一个是正面一个是反面则布拉德获胜，两个同时为正面或同时为反面则皮特获胜。你认为谁获胜的概率更大一些？

参考答案

互动练习 1：
①C　②B　③B

互动练习 4：
①蓝　②黄　③蓝　④绿

互动练习 2：
他用雨伞的机会不多。　$\frac{3}{31}$

互动练习 5：
$\frac{1}{4}$

互动练习 3：
①因为棒棒糖的数量最少，摸到的概率也就小。
②布拉德最可能摸到巧克力。
③他可以依据糖的形状摸。

互动练习 6：
4种　$\frac{1}{4}$

互动练习 7：
布拉德和皮特获胜的概率一样大。

（习题设计：骆　双）

Bad Luck Brad

Brad rubbed his eyes. He sat up in bed. Then he saw the clock: 7:45.

"Oh, no!" he cried. He had overslept—and on the last day of school. There was going to be a party, and everything!

Brad ran downstairs.

On the way, he bumped into his sister, Lauren, and his brother, Adam. Then he tripped over a toy. "Oh, man!" he muttered.

Brad got to the kitchen after everyone else.

"Looks like we all overslept," said Dad. "No eggs or pancakes this morning."

Mom held out a bag of breakfast bars. "Everyone reach in and take one," she said.

The label on the bag read, "Lots of chocolate-chip bars! Lots of lemon-lime bars!" But Brad knew there weren't lots of chocolate-chip bars. He had eaten most of them.

"I want chocolate chip!" Adam said.

"Me too!" said Lauren.

"So do I," said Brad.

Everyone reached.

"Not so fast!" said Mom. She shook the bag. Lots of lemon-lime bars fell out—and only two chocolate-chip bars.

"Uh-oh," Brad said. "Two chocolate-chip bars—and three kids." He crossed his fingers for luck.

"I want to be fair," Mom said. She put the breakfast bars back into the bag. "You can each take out one bar. Lauren came into the kitchen first, so she'll go first. Then Adam, then Brad. No peeking!"

Lauren reached inside. "Ugh! Lemon-lime!" she said.

"My turn," said Adam. "Lucky me!" he yelled. "Chocolate-chip!"

" Now there's only one chocolate-chip bar left," Brad thought. He reached into the bag. "Unlucky me," he said. "Lemon-lime."

Brad sighed. He wanted the last day of school to be great. But already everything was going wrong.

Mom dropped Brad and his friend Pete at school. "I'll pick you up at the Candy Arcade," she said. "And then we'll do something special."

"Like a movie?" asked Brad.

"Like a movie," said his mom.

"Let's see *Space Flight 5!*" cried Brad. "I loved *4, 3, 2,* and *1!*"

"No way!" said Pete. "I want to see *Dinosaur Days!*"

"*Space Flight!*" said Brad as they handed in books.

"*Dinosaur Days!*" said Pete as they cleaned out their desks.

"It's time for our party!" said Mrs. Costa. "Everyone put their grab-bag presents on the table."

"Yes!" cried Brad.

His present was an action figure—Commander Cody, hero of the *Space Flight* movies. He wanted it himself.

"I brought in T-Rex," Pete whispered.

"Cool," Brad said.

Brad wondered what the other presents were. Paul's present was wrapped in dinosaur paper. He could hear Zach say, "I brought Commander Cody."

"Lots of great stuff," said Brad. "Maybe I'll be lucky."

Brad heard Lisa whisper to Ella. "I brought a pony of *Pony Parade.* So did Annie, Abby, and Sara."

"Humph," said Brad. He didn't want a silly pony. He didn't want any of the girl presents.

"Time for the grab bag!" said Mrs. Costa. "Just pick a name from this hat. Then go to the table and take the present with that name on it."

Everyone started lining up.

Brad looked at all the presents. Then it hit him. There were way more girls in the class than boys. So it was way more likely that he would pick a girl's name. "I'll probably wind up with a pony," he whispered, "instead of something I really want."

It was Brad's turn. He pulled out a name—Abby. "Oh no!" he said. "I'm getting a pony." He unwrapped the present anyway.

"You are so lucky!" squealed Sara. "You got Pretty Pal the Palomino."

Lucky? Brad didn't feel lucky. He felt like Bad Luck Brad.

Ella unwrapped her present. "Commander Cody!" she said. "Just what I wanted!"

Brad sighed.

"Brad!" Lisa said. "I picked your name! What did you bring?"

"Commander Cody," he said.

Lisa made a face.

"Hey!" Brad said. "Do you want to trade?"

"Sure!" said Lisa.

Just then the bell rang. School was over—for the whole entire summer!

Brad and Pete raced to the Candy Arcade. "I want a sour-peach T-Rex," Pete said.

"I want a gumball," Brad said. "A red one."

Brad looked at all the gumballs. The first machine had mostly white ones. The second had yellow and purple. The third machine had white, yellow, purple, green, black—and red, too!

Pete swallowed the last bit of his T-Rex. "I think I'll have a white gumball," he said. He put a quarter in the first machine. Out rolled a white gumball.

Brad dropped a quarter in the last machine. "Come on, red!" he shouted. Plop! Out came a white gumball.

Brad handed the gumball to Pete. "Your're lucky. You got what you wanted—twice!"

Pete grinned. "That's because I try the machines that have a lot of what I like."

"I know," said Brad. "But none of the machines have lots of red, so I probably won't get a red gumball."

"You like purple gumballs, too," Pete said. "And this machine has plenty of purple!"

"I'll try it," said Brad. He put his last quarter in the slot. What came out? A yellow gumball.

Pete shook his head. "I guess it's never a sure thing. Here, I have another quarter."

"Maybe one more try," Brad said.

Beep! Beep! It was Brad's mom.

"Too late now," said Pete. "Come on. Let's go to see *Dinosaur Days!*"

"No," said Brad, "*Space Flight!*"

They ran to the car.

"Let's see when the movies are playing," said Mom. "We need a 4:00 show."

She opened the newspaper. "*Space Flight* is playing in five theaters, and *Dinosaur Days* in just one."

Brad grinned. There was a good chance the time would be right for *Space Flight*. It was playing in lots of theaters!

"*Dinosaur Days* is playing at 5:15," said Mom. "But *Space Flight* is playing at 3:30, 4:00, 4:30, 5:00, and 5:30."

"You said 4:00!" Brad shouted. "We get to see *Space Flight!*"

Pete sighed.

"I'm sorry," Brad told Pete. He knew just how Pete was feeling. Then he remembered something.

"Next time we can see *Dinosaur Days*," he said. "We'll have lots of chances. It's summer VACATION!"